DEADLY SHE-WOLF ASSAS
Soundtrack R

D1430875

1. THE WAY OF THE WOLF (4:50)
2. IMPERIAL INTRIGUE (2:00)
3. ENTER: THE SHE-WOLF SECRET WEAPON (3:05)
4. 'ROUND AND 'ROUND HADES WE GO! (5:01)
5. IN THE SHADOW OF THE WOLF (2:16)
6. NIGHTMARES (3:09)
7. IN A SILENT WAY I SEEK MY PREY (5:25)
8. THE COMING OF THE THREE HURRICANES (1:00)
9. BOK MEI: THE WHITE LOTUS OF
   THE KING KONG PALM OF DEATH (7:01)
10. COLONEL ULYSSES SAM ARMAGEDDON (4:27)
11. QASEEM THE KILLING MACHINE (6:13)
12. THE STORM OF THE SHE-WOLF (2:06)
13. WE HAVE ARRIVED IN HELL (4:20)
14. PICK UP THE SWORD TO DEFEAT
    THE SWORD: END OF THE ASSASSIN (1:13)

Total Time: 52:12

MOMMA'S SONG
(music and concept based upon and inspired by Archie Shepp's *Blasé*)

Music by Archie Shepp (1969)/Fred Ho (2005)
Written by Christine Stark

15. **Exposition/Momma's Song** (Ar. Fred Ho, Words by Christine Stark) (14:44)
16. **Development/Momma's Song** (Ar. Fred Ho, Words by Christine Stark) (4:41)
17. **Transcendence Coda** (Fred Ho) (0:56)

Total Time: 20:21

innova® Recordings is the label of the American Composers Forum.
332 Minnesota Street E-145, St. Paul, MN 55101
Philip Blackburn: Director
Chris Campbell: Operations Manager
www.innova.mu

1

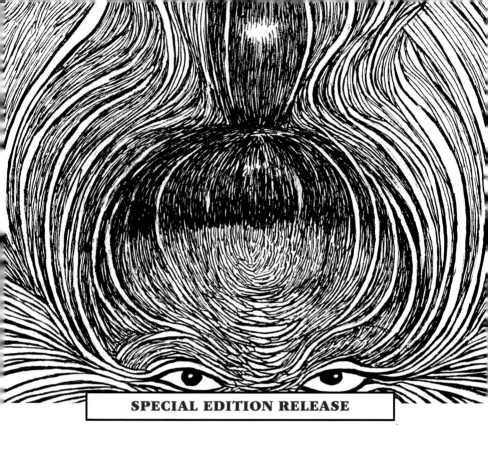

The old Fred Ho died August 4, 2006 of advanced colo-rectal cancer. Fred Ho, composer-baritone saxophonist-band leader-opera/multi-media producer and creator of Afro Asian epics and manga music/theater, had a vast body of new work recorded, some fully realized as theatrical stage productions, others unrealized, prior to his death.

The new Fred Ho, born August 5, 2006, introduces these never before released sound tracks of two grand works: the instrumental sound track to **DEADLY SHE-WOLF ASSASSASSIN AT ARMAGEDDON!** (a manga opera) and **MOMMA'S SONG**, an epic cosmo-poem by native American writer

Christine Stark of a horrific and brutal tale of genocide, ecocide and matricide visited upon Turtle Island, and created as a tribute to Archie Shepp, whose classic signature work of the Black Arts Movement, *Blasé*, had a profound impact upon the old Fred Ho. This recording is dedicated to Mr. Shepp.

This special edition release features the entirety of both texts, **SHE-WOLF** written by the late Ho and Ruth Margraff, and Stark's dark-as-night **MOMMA'S SONG**, as well as illustrations by Mac McGill to convey Fred Ho's musical manga imagination.

DEADLY SHE·WOLF

ASSASSIN AT ARMAGEDDON!

Music and Concept by Fred Ho
Written by Fred Ho & Ruth Margraff
Illustrations by Mac McGill

© Fred Ho and Ruth Margraff/Transformation Art Publisher 2005
Commissioned by 2005 NYSCA Individual Artist award to Ruth Margraff
through The Japan Society. Presented as part of The Japan Society's city-wide exhibit
"Cool Japan: Otaku Strikes!" to sold out performances April 29-30, 2005.

Book design and Illustrations by Arabelle Clitandre

Fred Ho (baritone sax, leader), Masaru Koga (alto sax, shakuhachi, fue)
Art Hirahara (piano and electronic keyboard), Wesley Brown (electric bass)
Royal Hartigan (drums and percussion) Yumi Kurosawa (20 string koto)

Engineer: Jon Rosenberg.
Recorded at Studio Masuo NYC on June 26, 2006.
Mixed, Edited and Mastered July 2, 2006.

Published by Transformation Art Publisher (ASCAP), 2006.
www.spectrummusic.net / www.bigredmediainc.com

Supported in part by a grant from
the Aaron Copland Fund for Music Recording Program

DEADLY SHE·WOLF ASSASSIN
AT ARMAGEDDON
NOTES

**Production History of
Stage Production (as of 2006)**
Directed by Sonoko Kawahara
Choreographed by Tsuyoshi Kaseda
Lighting by Carolyn Wong
Costumes by Coleen Scott

April 29 and 30, 2005 first act, work-in-progress performances at The Japan Society, New York City, cast: Aikiko Aizawa (She-wolf); Yoshi Amao (Lone Rogue Assassin); Mei-chiao Chiu (The Boy); Statoshi Okabe (Shogun/Ninja/Samurai); Takumi Bando (Iyagu/Ninja/Samurai); Ai Ikeda (Sister She-wolf/Ninja); Emmanuel Brown (Ninja/Samurai); Dawn Akemi Saito (Narrator); Yukako Yamazoe (Production Stage Manager).

June 24 and 25, 2006 world premiere, Mandel Theater @ Drexel University, Philadelphia, PA, cast: Ai Ikeda (She-wolf); Yoshi Amao (Lone Rogue Assassin); Takemi Kitamura (The Boy); Kerry Huang (The Shogun/Ninja/Samurai); Takumi Bando (Iyagu); Mika Saburi (Sister She-wolf/Ninja); Airon Armstrong (Colonel USA/Ninja/Samurai); Satoshi Okabe (Bok Mei Lotus/Ninja/Samurai); Vaughn Nelson (Qaseem/Ninja/Samurai); Marina Celander (Narrator); Jan Mizashima (Production Stage Manager). Special thanks to Thaddeus Squire and Peregrine Arts, Inc.; Yoko Shioya and the staff of The Japan Society.

Notes from Fred Ho
Everything I create starts with the music. From 1972 to 1974, six of the original *Lone Wolf and Cub* chambara (Japanese martial arts/samurai period) films were released and quickly ignited an international cult following. This cinematic output coincided with the first renaissance of Hong Kong kung fu films and U.S. black exploitation cinema, respectively. The *Lone Wolf* film music by composers Hideakira Sakurai (who composed the first five film scores) and Kunihiko Murai (who did the last, sixth film), in my opinion, ranks among the greatest movie-television music of all time, including the espionage film music of Lalo Schriffin (the classic *Mission: Impossible* tv series and *Enter: The Dragon*), Curtis Mayfield's *Superfly* score, Ennio Moriccone's spaghetti western soundtracks and the sword and sandal and sci-fi fantasy scores of Bernard Hermann. The music for the *Lone Wolf* movies innovatively combines Japanese traditional influences with the hippest of contemporary "jazz". In the film music, there is virtually no melody. Rather, texture and rhythm abound. I've tried to retain this approach in my score. The only "thematic motif" is a three-note

descending line (whole step to half step *ala* traditional Japanese *iwato* mode) and a four-note ascending figure (minor third-whole step-whole step) evocative of a clarion jazz-blues riff or the first four of five notes in a primal pentatonic mode. I've upped the musical intensity with increased metrical complexity, more "free" improvisation and greater layering of cross- and poly-rhythms, while at the same time retained much of the flowing, poignant "minimalism" of traditional Japanese music-theater.

Why chose assassins as "heroes" or central characters? In an era of social upheaval and transition as was the case of the twilight era of the Tokugawa period of Edo-Japan (mid-19th century), and the ominous arrival and contact with The West, the traditional values become diluted, distorted, corrupted, perverted and inverted. When political and moral corruption abound, the assassin or anti-hero who rejects all rules, forsakes all loyalty to the established order and embraces the cold-blooded capitalist way of "professional for hire" becomes the apotheosis of revolutionary individualism tearing asunder all feudal obligations and ascriptions. And yet, the Assassin and his son, always referred to as "we" ("We, father and son, have chosen to live in the world of blood shedding/We are not afraid to face any danger, known or unknown/We live at the crossroads of Hell"), disgraced and who in turn discard social position and proprieties, become the greatest threat to imperial decadence and arrogance.

It has been a joy to collaborate again with writer Ruth Margraff and we give our thanks to Yoko Shioya and her staff at The Japan Society for all of their support and enthusiasm for this project in its initial development and work-in-progress showing in New York, and especially to Thaddeus Squire and Peregrine Arts for the world premiere in Philadelphia.

Notes from Ruth Margraff:

In 2003, I traveled to Tokyo, Japan to study Noh at the National Noh Theater through Theater Nohgaku. I then attended Noh workshops in Bloomsburg and at New Dramatists through Theater Nohgaku and have found the structure of Noh influencing two of my recent plays that end in Noh plays. In 2004, I spent some time in Austin, Texas writing Stadium Devildare for the Rude Mechanicals which was inspired by the Japanese novel/film/manga *Battle Royale* and the Yukio Mishima novella *Patriotism*. I noticed that a majority of Austin theater artists had day jobs dubbing anime films into English and that there is the thriving annual anime Ushicon Festival downtown in major Texas cities. I had already started collecting the Kazuo Koike & Goseki Kojima *Lone Wolf & Cub* Dark Horse manga books as research with Fred Ho years ago and I got excited by how many vintage and pop Japanese icons are enjoying a burgeoning popularity among American kids and adults. Both Noh and anime have deeply influenced the creation of the She-Wolf character who has been fatefully stirred to avenge a myth distilled in her very soul. She has to shift the centrifuge of her vengeance onto the Assassin/Lone Wolf's Boy, the only one who has no blood upon his hands.

I think both our She-Wolf and Rogue Assassin characters, like the hero of the *Lone Wolf & Cub* films, speak to me because they have been struck by fate rather than by a traditional American dream. First in being given the bloody office of counter-assassin, and then by being hunted and hated by the Empire and all its minions in eventual exile. They are brutally instinctual in mercenary vengeance. They travel the same road to Hell, living like demons. And yet, in doing so, there is an unbreakable loyalty in each to son or father and to a cause that is beyond any institutional intuition. In this, we are taught true independence and integrity through the inferno that we do not often learn from our monolithically aggressive leaders in America today. Our She-Wolf Assassin is never number one or super-powerful. She never moves unilaterally, but rather—like a wolf—preys upon the most corrupted fangs of parasitic power, that threatens the survival of the pack.

I would like to especially thank the martial artists, Sonoko, Tsuyoshi and The Japan Society together with my dear long-time collaborator Fred Ho, for inspiring in our generation the vibrance of training, excellence, justice and honor in the rare way of the Wolf.

Raised as a weapon by a brutal conspirator, a young female assassin discovers that her target has spun the empire of Japan into crisis and ruin-and-is none other than her father. The Shogun, in a rage, has fired her master and hired three super warriors from the West to eliminate this Last Wolf of Japan who defies his legacy. Torn between loyalty to her mission, her nation and her soul, she must face the unimaginable at the twilight of an imperial epoch.

CHARACTERS

SHE·WOLF

Illegitimate daughter of THE ROGUE ASSASSIN, raised as secret counter-assassin weapon by IYAGU in the Shadow of the Wolf.

THE ROGUE ASSASSIN

A disgraced Kaishakunin (the SHOGUN's official executioner, also referred to as "The Second", i.e., second-in-command only to the Shogun) who became an assassin for hire after the murder of his wife, which he seeks to avenge.

THE BOY

Son of THE ROGUE ASSASSIN, at 10 years old, has seen countless deaths and horrors with his father.

THE SHOGUN

Desperate despot at the twilight of his imperial epoch.

IYAGU

A conspirator from the brutal Yagyu clan (much like Othello's Iago)responsible for the murder of THE ROGUE ASSASSIN's wife and subsequent disgrace; enraged that the assassin has been able to foil all attempts upon his life, no matter how sophisticated; filled with festering obsession to destroy the Assassin once and for all, whatever the cost. Old man now but still deadly and vicious, wears an eye-patch of pure evil.

THE 3 ARMAGEDDON, INC.
SUPERWARRIORS

3 hurricanes imagineered by Armageddon Inc. Trained killers with extraordinary martial abilities hired by SHOGUN to kill THE ROGUE ASSASSIN;

BOK MEI LOTUS,
CHINESE SUPERWARRIOR

Master of the King Kong death palm fighting style. Once a Shaolin sell-out, betrayer of the Shaolin Temple. Psychofrenetic part monk, part lustful spiritual traitor, the only one of the 10 famous Canton tigers living in infamy. Like the renegade monk in *Iron Monkey*.

COLONEL USA
(ULYSSES SAM ARMAGEDDON)
WESTERN SUPER-WARRIOR

Fighting style "old hickory" alligator. CIA-spy, James Bond type of colonial intrigue plotter, well-spoken and intellectual, sophisticated and lettered debonair of the military aristocracy known for slaughtering prisoners of war. Part General Custer/Ulysses Grant/Andrew Jackson. Tough, cruel, calm and patient, a political traitor and extreme venture capitalist.

QASEEM THE KILLING MACHINE
BLACK SUPERWARRIOR

Fighting style panther. A professional mercenary jetsetter, ultimate elegant killing machine with cotton gin efficiency. Ruthless and bound to no laws, no nation or location. A trans-national figure who once profited from the slave trade of his people. A race traitor. Helped in the destruction of the greater Islamic empire. An exile with all the dirty tricks of fighting stolen from all over the world. Closest thing to THE ROGUE ASSASSIN. Like Kareem Abdul-Jabbar in *Game of Death*. Like Houson Djimon playing the Kazari Bomani character in *Alias* Season 3 episodes "Unveiled", "The Frame" and "Repercussions" #17,18 and 5.

NINJAS & SAMURAI

There are two forces of trained mercenary ninjas and samurai serving the SHOGUN and IYAGU against THE ROGUE ASSASSIN. The SHOGUN's forces have dwindled to ruin, and IYAGU no longer has an army other than the SHE-WOLF and her loyalists used in her training. She is his last secret weapon. THE ROGUE ASSASSIN has destroyed the bulk of both their forces down to a few brutal survivors of the chaos and the foreign reinforcements.

NARRATOR

Knows past, present and future. Enacts the thoughts, subtext and speech of all the characters.

ACT I.

Scene 1.
THE WAY OF THE WOLF

Scene 2.
IMPERIAL INTRIGUE

Scene 3.
ENTER: THE SHE-WOLF SECRET WEAPON

Scene 4.
THE COMING OF THREE HURRICANES

Scene 1. THE WAY OF THE WOLF
Pitched sword battle rages with samurai and
ninja warriors protecting the target of the
ROGUE ASSASSIN which he eliminates with
virtuosity. His BOY watches in the shadows,
ten years old. Music.

Scene 2. IMPERIAL INTRIGUE
In the wake of slaughter in the background, as
if behind closed doors, IYAGU is revealed to be
gnashing his teeth at the elegant
feet of the SHOGUN.

NARRATOR
[SHOGUN in imperial voice]

Iyagu, hunh. For ten years! You failed to eliminate my former
Kaishakunin—who was once my official executioner and my second. He is now known
as masterless and mercenary—ROGUE ASSASSIN? Has he eluded you or something?
What happened to the heads I commanded to be hacked off still dangling by some
thread? Why is my empire in a crisis? Why are my forces decimated? Why do my lords
defy me? How could you let this happen you feeble old goat?

**[IYAGU shudders, bowing, grumbling with rage like a low roar in his
teeth, thoughts racing in his head]:**

[IYAGU]

My imperial shogun, I sent the black wind dragnet to kill the
Rogue Assassin's wife and his servants...

[SHOGUN]

Why did you aggravate him? Why did you set him off to carve his crazy path to
Hell? Why did you let him and his Boy escape, recover and he flourishes?

[IYAGU growling]

I sent the gateless warriors and the peasant ninja whores…

[SHOGUN]

Why has this Rogue Assassin denounced the sacred code of Samurai, refused to kill
himself as I commanded, and he's taken on the path of a Demon? To eclipse my
legacy? And not just me by the way he has defied us all…yourself included, but who
cares about Iyagu hunh? Why has this Rogue Assassin drained my wealth and splat-
tered my roads and mountains with the blood of my finest warriors in Japan? I think I
gave you power to take care of him. Well you fail and I am taking you off the job. You
are an insult to my nation, you are no longer competent!

[IYAGU under his breath]

Not even the shadow grass elite could cut him down…

NARRATOR
[SHOGUN]

So it is with great fear, desperation and-- and shame that I consider now a foreign solution. I think I hire now three sons of the west in a cabal to shame the honor of Japan and shame myself and shame you too. It is an egregious thing, a loss of face, a sacrilege for you to bear upon your soul throughout the epoch of Edo.

Scene 3. ENTER: THE SHE-WOLF
SECRET WEAPON
Later. IYAGU still muttering with rage from the SHOGUN'S rebuke, reveals his trump card.

[IYAGU]

No one in Japan can touch the devil…Rogue Assassin… Now the unthinkable humiliation to both country and to myself: the Shogun will bring 3 foreign hurricanes he hopes will finally kill the Rogue Assassin. To soak more blood upon the road to Hell. The Shogun has been duped again. For I gloat still in the heart of Edo. I will make my own deal with the west, my own execution of the executioner, cut in two and rivers of red still flowing in his dreams and hunted like a dog wherever he goes… But I have one more secret. One last weapon stashed away for the end of the world… there shall arise a daughter of vengeance! . . !

[The SHE-WOLF demonstrates her training by IYAGU, a martial arts solo demonstrating 1. fan as exotic weapon 2. ninja scarf as deadly whip and 3. hand-to-hand combat, etc.]

[IYAGU]

Ah yes my stealthy saboteur, the last Wolf of Japan, my little She-Wolf. Trained from birth to be my final weapon! Illegitimate bastard of the Rogue Assassin himself (unbeknownst to anyone on earth), stolen away from a forgotten whore he used to prove a point in some rebellion. Sprung from a test of will and slaughter…Ah yes, this way,

[SHE-WOLF]

My lord. To demonstrate my training.

[IYAGU releases a female ninja. The SHE-WOLF cuts her in half in mid-air, a streak like red silk of her life-blood.]

[IYAGU]

Your living hands and steady soul, you hold the fire to your back and don't be furrowed. Think of nothing but of cutting.

NARRATOR

[SHE-WOLF]

I demonstrate my loyalty by slaying my loyalist sister who sacrificed
her life for my training.

[IYAGU]

Think only of the cutting, cutting, of that one, lone Rogue Assassin, drain the life of
him in slashes, where he is the weakest, out of balance, at the corners, death at every
turn and never late, be useful, useful. . .

[SHE-WOLF]

I take on the ferocity of every life I take to fuel my vengeance on these coward
mercenaries who betray Japan.

[IYAGU]

Knowing well the void that does not yet exist and know the void that is and was, and
every trifle, every rise and fall.

[SHE-WOLF]

I am cut loose from love and sorrow.
I live the hour of the Wolf.

**[Ends in a final test of wills where the SHE-WOLF cuts down an
onslaught of samurai who spring upon her to demonstrate her
formidable arrogance and prowess.]**

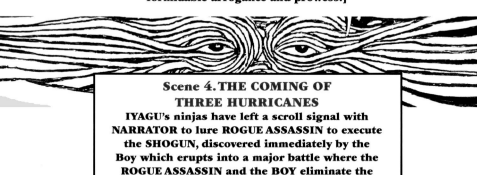

**Scene 4. THE COMING OF
THREE HURRICANES**
**IYAGU's ninjas have left a scroll signal with
NARRATOR to lure ROGUE ASSASSIN to execute
the SHOGUN, discovered immediately by the
Boy which erupts into a major battle where the
ROGUE ASSASSIN and the BOY eliminate the
ninja messengers as they know
immediately it is a trap.**

NARRATOR

[SHE-WOLF TO BOY]

When you were a baby, after your mother was slain, your father let you choose his fate. Between the ball and the sword. You chose the sword. Why don't you hold it now.

[The same battle repeats itself however in the mind of the BOY later in his nightmares. BOY turns and sees a girl in the shadows of the fight who has come secretly to the aid of his father. BOY stops her in mid strike, terrified.]

[SHE-WOLF]

That time I was helping you. Yes, I've been assisting you for quite some time. In the shadow of the Wolf. Void as the wind. How did you think one man and a boy could be invincible for so long against so many well-trained enemies. If you call now for your father I will vanish to the shadows of your mind so deeply they will question your own sanity as to whether I exist at all. I allow my spirit to appear to you alone. Your father will never see me unless I will that. This is my training. What do I want from you? To help you reach the heart of Edo? I know your father knows this Edo scroll is a trap laid to ensnare you. What you don't know is that Iyagu has at last turned against his precious Shogun and would like to help your father kill the Shogun and seize power because the Shogun has betrayed Japan. Iyagu has come to believe in the way of the assassin, staying true to the enemy of one's true enemy.

This is the end of the epoch of the Shogun. The beginning of the epoch of the lone Rogue cut loose from all aristocratic ties. The lone worker who owes nothing and owns nothing and must sell his labor for his wage. Iyagu would like to sell your father his own cunning. What is the wage you ask. The Shogun's own head rolling in a puddle of revolt. That may seem blasphemous. But is it really? To one spawned from a demon? Don't try to ask your father his advice or I will vanish everytime you try to tell on the shadow that does not exist. You will never know when I am helping you. Or hindering.

[She vanishes. Another battle ensues. The ROGUE ASSASSIN wins, seemingly easily.]

[BOY]

Leave us alone.

NARRATOR

[SHE-WOLF]
I have to do my job.

[BOY]

We don't need you. My father is the fiercest Wolf Japan has ever known.

[SHE-WOLF]
Little braggart **[laughs]**. We shall see what wolves are lurking from beyond Japan. There shall descend three hurricanes upon your father from the mountains…BOK MEI LOTUS, MASTER OF THE KING KONG DEATH PALM!

from the sea…
COLONEL ULYSSES SAM ARMAGEDDON, Chief Executive Officer of
ARMAGEDDON, INC.!

and from the sky…
QASEEM THE KILLING MACHINE!

> As the BOY's mind is clouded by the ambush spectacle of the 3
> foreign super warriors, SHE-WOLF covertly uses his amazement
> to camouflage her kidnapping of the BOY finally from his father,
> the ROGUE ASSASSIN. SHE-WOLF binds the BOY in her ninja
> sash, dragged quickly to the feet of her master, IYAGU,
> who rushes headlong with the prize.

ACT II.

Scene 1. WE WILL BE GLORIOUS,
A FEAST OF FOOLS

In the SHOGUN's fortress, an apprehensive celebration is at hand. In the distance roars the agony of the ROGUE ASSASSIN, slaughtering the warriors left who camouflaged his son's abduction. IYAGU rushes ahead dragging the boy with SHE-WOLF at alert around them, to Edo where they will find the SHOGUN waiting. As IYAGU parades THE BOY before the SHOGUN, he gloats with wicked, excited thoughts.

[IYAGU]

A perfect strategy, my weapon, yes, my She-Wolf. Indigenous, expendable, unseen, go to your shadow. Now that I have the boy I can fall back into the graces of the Shogun. I have done what was unthinkable! How did I manage this, oh yes it's working very well. To shift the centrifuge of our most hunted, hated fugitive onto that fragile bond of son and father! As long as the boy lives, ah, the Rogue will wreak his vengeance on me. I should have strangled the infant 10 years ago in its mother's blood. But better now, a public execution... The Rogue will follow, drawn at last to the heart of Edo. My final trap where my saboteur will sabotage and kill—kill—kill—

[Stops to look at SHE-WOLF, then rushes on.]

Or let the superwarriors kill him, kill the Shogun then, or just kill boy, kill Rogue, kill Shogun, either way, kil—kill—the—

[To SHE-WOLF] I forbid you to speak to anyone at the feast. But dress up anyway. To the nines.

[SHE-WOLF]
No name, no art, no trace but shadows.

[BOY]
Where is my father?

[SHE-WOLF]
Without you he will have no lineage. No future.

[BOY]
Are those your thoughts or your command?

[SHE-WOLF]
Don't let my master see you talking in my silent way.

[BOY]
I trusted you.

[SHE-WOLF]
And I am with you now.

NARRATOR

[SHOGUN]

You old goat Iyagu. **[IYAGU flinches]** Still cunning are you. To abduct the last seed of the wild dog! Ah yes, I hear his distant pain! Slaughtering what's left of the wake of our abduction oh so swiftly done! amidst my world-class ambush of the superwarrior hurricanes! We must enjoy this moment. I've been waiting so long for a feast.

[SHOGUN gestures for the pomp and circumstance to commence, for the superwarriors to gather, and orders QASEEM to take charge of holding the BOY. He then babbles on into the night, long-winded in a gloating speech.]

[SHOGUN]

We will be glorious again. We will be grand. With such great fortress, might and muscle we prevail against this Last Wolf of Japan and entertain his execution for tomorrow. You see I have been fortifying Edo. I now parade my arsenal and forces swollen now with valour! Even if we lost ten thousand warriors and ten thousand years. We come away now with the boy. Bastard of the last insurgence. His Father groveling after him. And now the time has come for us. Our victory…our triumph, revelry and our glory is here at hand. It is upon us. It is near us. It is…

[BOK MEI LOTUS]

It is time for Bok Mei Lotus Superwarrior to inflict his Mastery of King Kong death palm fighting style on that Lone Assassin dog at the gates of Edo as he arrives. It is time for the gluttony of pleasure laced with agony. Time for the first psychofrenetic cannibal among the Shaolin monks of China. (I recommended the scent of that to all those bald-headed vegan Buddhists mumbling at their prayers when I sold out the Shaolin Temple to the renegades.) It is time for the only one of the 10 canton tigers living in infamy. It is time for Bok Mei Lotus! Hater and betrayer of Shaolin, thief of the King Kong death palm secret scroll!

[He illustrates the King Kong death palm throughout.]

So all the rest of you go back to sleep or watch the end of all the troubles of Japan. I got the Bok Mei Lotus special forces lined up, well-prepared, and triple-fortified the walls to be impenetrable! You may have a problem with the way I party but this is it. Cause I will have whoever this bitch is tonight.

[Thumps himself in naked lust at SHE-WOLF.]

Scene 2. THE GATES OF HELL
(vs. BOK MEI LOTUS)
ROGUE ASSASSIN at the gates of Edo, releases
smoke bomb grenades from his special armored
vest that carries also other special weapons.

NARRATOR
[SHOGUN]

But alas! What is this plume of smoke?!?! My army here, in rank and file, hurled to a
wall of warriors. The strong gates of Edo, crumbling into sand! My soldiers cough
and stagger to the ground! I explode my temper too amid this carnage, not as planned.
My massive men coagulating in cold blood. It is impossible to see! The Bok Mei Lotus
death squads blindly crammed together in a nuisance to itself. Hacking at each other
like the weeds along the road to Hell. Something carving its way through the writhing
stench with cold, steel eyes and a Dotanuki sword... Who are you! Lone Rogue Assassin?!?

[BOK MEI LOTUS]

I am BOK MEI LOTUS. I can cut through torsos easily with my amazing
death palm fighting style. I don't need my soldiers. I can clear their corpses with my
King Kong death palm. I will prove my force is still superior to any
hemorrhage riot. But what is this.

[As the toxic smoke clears and the final soldier falls, leaving just BOK MEI
LOTUS and the ROGUE ASSASSIN Face off. Okay, Let's go.]

[The Shaolin traitor faces off against the ROGUE ASSASSIN.]

[Fight scenic note: ROGUE ASSASSIN primarily dodges the devastating
King Kong palm. Uses sword but it is clear the force of BOK MEI LOTUS
is superior. ROGUE ASSASSIN stabs BOK MEI LOTUS in a special move.
ROGUE ASSASSIN fakes being hit by King Kong palm. Falls on his knee.
ROGUE akes out small dagger,gauges out his eye.]

[BOK MEI LOTUS]

Unjust! That is the closely-guarded eagle claw eye-poking-out technique! Nobody
knows that but the squirrelly monk I butchered when I aided and abetted
the destruction of Shaolin.

[ROGUE ASSASSIN uses BOK MEI LOTUS vanity and rage to get the other
eye, tender from the poisons of before. BOK MEI LOTUS flails in pain.
Uses King Kong palm too wildly. Wanders off, pounding
and roaring indiscriminately.]

Scene 3. ARMAGEDDON IN THE CITY
(vs. COLONEL USA—ULYSSES SAM ARMAGEDDON)
The SHOGUN and a few soldiers are left with COLONEL USA. QASEEM, in background can be seen chained to the BOY, head down.

NARRATOR
[COLONEL USA]

And so my Chinese colleague underestimated you. Can't trust an oriental to kill another oriental. When it's really a white man's job. Oh the Chinese looked down on the white barbarians and got so pompous with the gunpowder idea. Took the white man to apply it to the gun. I spit upon your martial arts. Your highly coveted kung fu.

Look at it now.

[Sidesteps the blinded, flailing BOK MEI LOTUS.]

Shall I recite my resume? My scorched earth policy. My superiority complex. Smart germs, settlement warfare, designer disease, rampant domestication, self-pollinating colonies spread out with cottin gin efficiency! And my printing press! To stratify the people into haves and have-nots! If I were you, I would have forced sterilization or extermination on all suspected rebels to begin with. I would have raped the spoils of their self-determination from day one. But I'm all about modernism. Why fight with a cutlass? When I've got a sixshooter to back me up against the lower pedigree of foe? Because my cutlass has survived so many aboriginies. To think of what it has been through! With its razor edge and blue-blood flourish. And to think that in the modern modernism this is old school. Ha!!!

[Fight scenic note: COLONEL USA shoves his cutlass into close quarters with the ROGUE ASSASSIN employing excellent techniques with every advantage of skilled intellect and science. The ROGUE ASSASSIN finds himself getting nicks here and there across his body and Japanese Dontuniki sword, allowing the greater arrogance of COLONEL USA to surge. Pick pockets the six-shooter. Lets COLONEL USA knock his sword out of hand.]

[COLONEL USA]

It's the white man's time now, sorry. Even if it takes a few more ornaments, West Point brutality will always prevail over the eastern goon. So I'll make this easy. I'll just get you in between the— agh!!

[COLONEL USA grabs for his holster. Realizes gun is missing. ROGUE ASSASSIN reaches in his sleeve, and shoots COLONEL USA between the eyes.]

[COLONEL USA as he is dying.]

I've killed the savages of all three continents. To spread my brand of freedom. It was my idea to bring you here to Edo, hah, my intelligence to that crony Iyagu pirate. I was feeling fine here, liked the scenery, the tiny food, the souvenirs you people fight with. I fought a tomahawk, a spear, a battle axe and canon but never did I expect this from my own six shooter. Never thought my own Smith & Wesson would turn against me. But I suppose if this is how I go, I'd rather go by my own hand than tortured the way I've made so many-die like a-like a... Bring it on.

[COLONEL. USA dies.]

Scene 4. SHOWDOWN WITH THE SHOGUN

NARRATOR
[SHOGUN]

I paid you foreigners a fortune and what do I get, one dead, one is humping at himself. My contract was for Armageddon, Inc. to have that Rogue Assassin apprehended by the time he got here to the feast of his own execution.

[Terrified and blubbering to IYAGU, having a nervous breakdown.]
Save me Iyagu. I know I have humiliated you. Guards, guards. They killed the mastermind, the manager, the... uh, I paid you didn't I, I paid the bill. I'll double the payment. I'll stoop to Iyagu, just make this go away. It's been too long. Too stressful. Please Iyagu! You there. The one called Qaseem The Killing Machine! You do it. Do something.

[IYAGU]

Ah the blood rush of my thoughts' crescendo! All my schemes laid out before me like a wicked banquet! The Shogun groveling, begging for my mercy. My life-long enemy unraveling before my eyes where I can kill him, kill the supermercenaries, kill the Shogun, kill the Boy, kill—

[IYAGU to SHOGUN, deadpan.]
Back in your graces just in time my lord.

[IYAGU maneuvers the SHOGUN toward the blinded BOK MEI LOTUS. BOK MEI's fist comes down hard on the SHOGUN, smashing his skull. SHE-WOLF kills BOK MEI LOTUS.]

[IYAGU to SHE-WOLF.]
Get rid of the evidence.

Scene 5. INSIDE GENOCIDE
(vs. QASEEM THE KILLING MACHINE)
SHOGUN's Palace Massacre. Private, elegant and brutal, inner chambers. QASEEM confronts the ROGUE ASSASSIN in the devastation for the first time. Walks around calmly, pulling the BOY like a rag doll, SHE-WOLF & IYAGU trailing behind.

[QASEEM]

Strictly business. All my business partners end up sniveling corpses in the end. So they mean nothing to me. Money is a blank. I had it. I had everything that this Chinese monk lusted for.

NARRATOR
[QASEEM]
[Explosively snaps BOK MEI LOTUS'S neck. Watches as BOK MEI LOTUS goes into death spasms.]

And this one here, this Custard of a man had gotten flabby in his science.
[Kicks COLONEL USA'S corpse out of the way.]

But I have to hand it to you. You conquered this particular franchise and they were the cream of a country or so. But I…was the prince of a continent. I sold my people to America as slaves to make a profit. I have been more cruel to my own than the colonialists. I resented my people more than any enemy and everyone is my enemy.

[IYAGU]
Just don't give up the boy. That was our only hostage. He is nothing without the boy. He has no power.

[QASEEM]
Shut up you old goat. **[IYAGU flinches with the insult.]**
I'm tired of being your babysitter. That's not why I'm part of Armageddon, Inc.

[QASEEM]
This boy is beneath me. Not a worthy opponent. I've had every power, kingdoms, my own nation, and the greater part of Africa. I didn't want to run it anymore. Sick and tired of politics, that dribble of the coward never mightier than the sword. There came, of course, a coup because of my brutalities, and the poor will always revolt. Which brought me to the business of transnational transmercenary…no land, no family, nobody but myself. And now I want just one thing. A decent challenge. To kill the greatest of the great. They promised me this chance to meet you, one on one and I see you are just like me. Not the pretty hero of rank and file. That was all too easy. You and I have never really been on the defensive. I have to say I've never seen such skill and ferocity as I have seen in this last hour. I took this job. But I turned down the money. I'm here just for the thrill, for the bounty without bounty. I am the ultimate insider genocider. I've burned every bridge to where I stand. I say we just go hand to hand. I am beholden to no blood, no law, no nation. I'm burned out on extinction. I fly no flag, but I hit like a plague. I just turned 28 and I'm the greatest of the great. And I'm here to be the end of you. No weapons.

[ROGUE ASSASSIN lowers his head slightly as QASEEM roars from his soul like the Alien from Predator, disarming himself before the fight to the death.]
Get out of the way, boy, I'm about to kill your father.

[QASEEM shoves the BOY down.]
Just bare hands. Bare knuckle homicide.

Scene 6. END OF ASSASSIN

QASEEM is winning over ROGUE ASSASSIN in a brutal one-on-one. But IYAGU, over-anxious, seeing his plans come together, orders SHE-WOLF to jump in to finish the ROGUE ASSASSIN. QUASEEM curses them both. It turns into 3-way battle. ROGUE ASSASSIN against QASEEM & SHE-WOLF.

[SHE-WOLF lunges but fails to intercept the Boy from IYAGU's clutches. ROGUE ASSASSIN and QASEEM begin to fight.]

NARRATOR
[QASEEM]
That's not the deal!!! The deal was one-on-one!

[QASEEM turns on both SHE-WOLF & ROGUE ASSASSIN as IYAGU taunts the ROGUE ASSASSIN with killing his boy in front of him. ROGUE gets second wind, QASEEM is weakening.]

[QASEEM]
I curse you stinkin' goat. I had the bastard. If you would've let me—one-on-one.
It was the perfect—

[ROGUE ASSASSIN & SHE-WOLF kill QASEEM together in one death blow. Continue fighting one-on-one.]

[IYAGU, gleefully boasting and gushing his schemes.]
Now is the moment of the She-Wolf, now. I raised you as my weapon for this very moment. Look into the eyes of the Last Wolf of Japan. You will see what you can recognize inside yourself. What I trained you to seek. To find this day, this moment. Everything I am, I've done for this. I was behind it and it followed us to where we stand. How I disgraced the Rogue Assassin ten years ago. I destroyed his wife and family. I raised you up believing you were the trash of a bastard, abandoned at birth, half dead. I told you I was the only father you would ever know. But you were the daughter of my daughter who disgraced my name. He took her like he's taken everything of mine. He never loved her, never knew her name, she didn't know his infamy. I banished her, forbid her, beat her, but still found her hiding from me with her wretched secret. My spies came after her for 8 months til they found her bundle, newly born. I hated you at first so deeply that I slashed your mother's heart in one death blow. I lifted you up in my hand to crush you in the river of your mother's blood, still red, still warm. And then the perfect scheme came over me. I seized you from your fate and put within your tiny hand the finest sword, the most exquisite training.
My final weapon. My She-Wolf.

[ROGUE ASSASSIN]
I give to you the one grace. I have given to no other. Only to my daughter.

[In blinding passion SHE-WOLF howls with agony as she marks a perfect blow on the back of the ROGUE ASSASSIN's throat.]

[Long silence as ROGUE ASSASSIN dies.]

[SHE-WOLF turning to the BOY, the only one left.]

[SHE-WOLF]
In the silhouettes of my inferno, distilled upon my soul…
You were both there…preying on the fangs of the corrupt…
that threaten the survival of the pack. I couldn't… fight you on my own.
Perhaps I've come to love you as your…father will love you always.
Without vengeance, without doubt…

[SHE-WOLF staggers with the revelation that her mother was killed by her master. Just as she is besting THE ROGUE ASSASSIN, IYAGU reaches out to kill the BOY with his secret dagger. With one hand SHE-WOLF slashes at IYAGU's heart, it flows with red. Flashback moment of the ball and sword.]

NARRATOR
[IYAGU]
And I predicted that as well. That you would turn against me. But I die now, I die now knowing you will function as I programmed your entire fate. I saw the Shogun on his knees, I saw my enemies fall before my eyes. I fall as well by my own weapon—

[IYAGU dies.]

[Disorients both SHE-WOLF and ROGUE ASSASSIN. ROGUE ASSASSIN shocked almost more, his worst nightmare. He sees the SHE-WOLF as if for the first time, what has been helping him. He had felt her strength, a strange power, for a while now. His injuries are mortal wounds. SHE-WOLF goes through her own internal struggle as she realizes the betrayal of her master that has left her programmed to kill her own father who is now dying by her hand.]

[SHE-WOLF]
I could always feel your strength. All my life. Across the fields. I forged my rhythms to your own. As I was trained. So I am loyal to the end. And now at last you feel my own strength now returned upon you. If you're really my father you didn't care about me. My life wasn't good. I don't remember any mother or father. If you are my father, then I curse you. What else would my life have been if I had known. I trained my whole life to deceive your Boy by helping you, thinking that Iyagu was my master, to ensnare you and your Boy. To bring us both to this. I am still loyal to my fate, to assassinate the assassin. I will finish the duty. You are just a target to me. As am I to you. The blood means nothing.

Only your Boy has this sacred bond to you because you loved his mother. Like me, my mother was just a mistake. Your Boy's mother wronged in a moment brought you to your fate together with the boy. A son fated to mean everything to you. I will bring your fate to bear now in the hour of the She-Wolf. Execution of the executioner at last. You are already cut and broken. You have slaughtered everyone along your path to hell. You can go now to that river of demons where you belong.

[The ROGUE ASSASSIN kneels down with his back to SHE-WOLF in the position of so many of his early victims when he was the SHOGUN's Second. Realizing it was himself that set in motion his own fate. That IYAGU'S hatred had much deeper roots than petty transgressions, higher clan and status.]

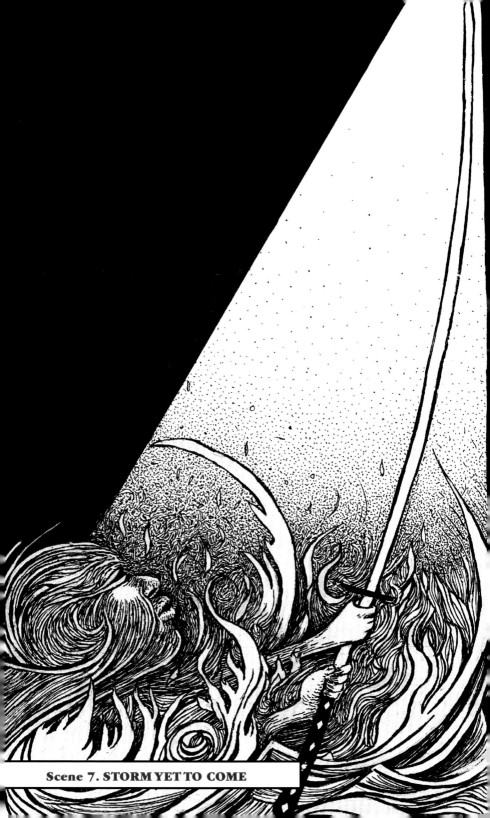

Scene 7. STORM YET TO COME

[There is apocalyptic destruction of everyone but the one who was not pre-
viously a warrior. During which SHE-WOLF is visible only from the front
in the deepening shadows. The BOY with father's sword and blood on it
comes into light. She moans from a blow behind her.]

NARRATOR
[SHE-WOLF]

Pick up the sword to defeat the sword. But when the sword has been defeated, you
must set it down. Still knowing how to use it. How to trust. To save the one with no
blood on his hands. Who had a father, thereby everything... Should hold onto that...

[The ball rolls through BOY's father's blood. She marks him with
her blood as his mother did when he was a baby, on his cheek.

Music as he watches the fire.

BOY walks into the path between heaven and hell,
carrying his father's sword.]

BIOS

Archie Shepp is a world-renown tenor and soprano saxophonist and composer and one of the leading artist-radicals who emerged during the Black Arts Movement of the 1960s.

Christine Stark is a writer, visual artist and activist of Anishinaabe, Cherokee, and European ancestry. She teaches writing at a community college in northern Minnesota. *Momma's Song* is for her ancestors and for the First Nation prostituted women who were murdered on a pig farm in Vancouver.

Fred Ho is a composer-baritone saxophonist, leader of the Afro Asian Music Ensemble and an acolyte and disciple of the Black Arts Movement (BAM). It has been his dream to do a redux version of this classic and under-recognized work from the BAM, to celebrate the prescience and genius of

Archie Shepp, and to support the talent of a powerful younger poetic voice such as Christine Stark.

Mac McGill's artwork has been published in many publications and his artwork is in the private collections of universties across the U.S. His word-less illustrated story of the 9/11 tragedy entitled *IX XI MMI* is in the permanent collection of The Library of Congress.

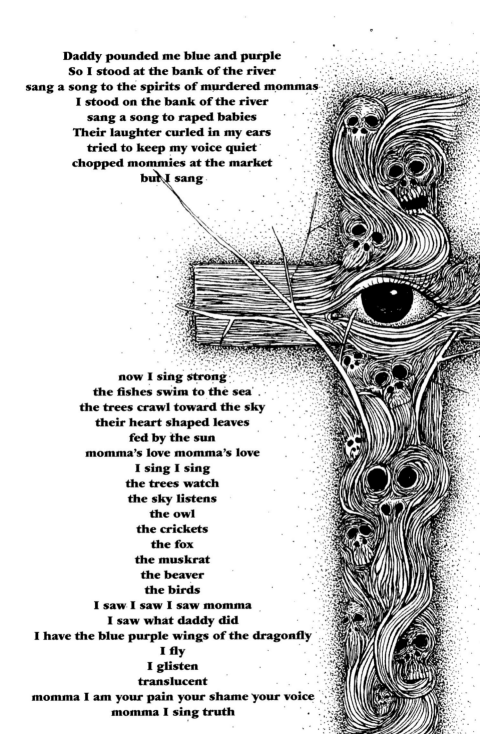

Daddy pounded me blue and purple
So I stood at the bank of the river
sang a song to the spirits of murdered mommas
I stood on the bank of the river
sang a song to raped babies
Their laughter curled in my ears
tried to keep my voice quiet
chopped mommies at the market
but I sang

now I sing strong
the fishes swim to the sea
the trees crawl toward the sky
their heart shaped leaves
fed by the sun
momma's love momma's love
I sing I sing
the trees watch
the sky listens
the owl
the crickets
the fox
the muskrat
the beaver
the birds
I saw I saw I saw momma
I saw what daddy did
I have the blue purple wings of the dragonfly
I fly
I glisten
translucent
momma I am your pain your shame your voice
momma I sing truth

Daddy pounded me blue and purple
dick ripped my mind
while the black robe man
with the gold and silver cross
the trapper
hunter
tree cutter
animal trader
soldier
earth digger
split their sides
about chopped mommies at the market
momma momma momma I cried
their cocky laughter ripped my insides
their laughing cocks
stole my voice
lost inside
daddy daddy why?
daddy daddy why?

women's blood covers the earth
glistening steel
runs rivers of blood
makes weapons that scar the earth
consuming all

Momma
I saw
what Daddy did
mommas torn from their babies
blood running deep converging on the sea
when I told
these Big Daddies split their sides
the joke of the century momma and me

But I saw what daddy did

I wandered over roads
found bits of me floating
under the moon
met raped babies
talked to spirits of murdered mommas
until my mind came back to me
my mind came back
the mommas and babies
told me to sing
sing my girl
sing for us

Daddy's steel
ran rivers of blood
down your legs
your screams took flight to the sky
the earth cried
the night broke blue granite
the dark tree limbs bent held me

Daddy took momma to the river
dumped her in the water
fed her
to the fishes
the fishes ate her
hair twisted 'round the tree roots
her body in the fishes
swam to the sea
momma momma come back to me
momma momma come back to me
momma momma come back to me
I screamed at 5 10 15 20
in the woods in the woods in the woods
momma disappeared

I told a priest
He said he'd pray
I told a doctor
He said he'd heard this before
then smiled
said: There's chopped mommy
for sale at the market.
And then he laughed
said to me: you're crazy.
I told a lawyer
He said: prove it.
I told a cop
He said: where's the body?
I said in the river in the river
in the river gone to the sea
in the heart shaped leaves
that grow on the bank

Daddy pushed pushed pushed
into you
ripped skin
his pistol dick shot your womb
one two three four times
five times
you screamed

Daddy was
the black robe man with a gold and silver cross
the trapper
the hunter
the tree cutter
the animal trader
the soldier man
the earth digger

stealing stealing stealing
us raw
slick slit cut deep
buried beneath the weight

the moon saw
the trees saw
the sky held your screams
the screams that cut us deep

Momma
i saw what Daddy did
100 200 300 400
500 years ago last night
the moonlight so white
the crushed wings of a dragonfly glistened
blue and purple on the black tar road

the colors of your face
the colors of your cunt
Daddy ripped raw red roses
made meat of your belly
Momma screamed
butchered
eyes wild with death
your baby left behind

Momma
I saw what Daddy
did
the night he ripped skin
shining beneath the moon
you cried
your pain
your shame
became mine

MOMMA'S SONG
NOTES

This work has never been performed. Christine Stark was commissioned by Fred Ho to create an cosmo-epic poem as a 21st century redux of Archie Shepp's 1969 work, *Blasé*.

Christine Stark writes:

MOMMA'S SONG is dedicated to the 69 missing prostituted women from Vancouver's Eastside, many of whom were First Nation women. Robert Pickton, a pig farmer, has been charged with the murder of 27 of the missing women. 60% of the women Pickton has been charged with murdering were First Nation women. The women's body parts were found on his farm, mixed with pig bones. Authorities believe that the women's bodies may have been processed with pig meat and given away."

Funding in part provided by Innova and the Aaron Copland Fund for Recording. Special thanks to Christine Stark, Archie Shepp, Jennifer Kidwell and Philip Blackburn.

SPECIAL EDITION RELEASE

The old Fred Ho died August 4, 2006 of advanced colo-rectal cancer. Fred Ho, composer-baritone saxophonist-band leader-opera/multi-media producer and creator of Afro Asian epics and manga music/theater had a vast body of new work recorded, some fully realized as theatrical stage productions, others unrealized, prior to his death.

The new Fred Ho, born August 5, 2006, introduces these never before released sound tracks of two grand works: the instrumental sound track to **DEADLY SHE-WOLF ASSASSASSIN AT ARMAGEDDON!** (a manga opera) and **MOMMA'S SONG**, an epic cosmo-poem by native American writer Christine Stark of a horrific and brutal tale of genocide, ecocide and matricide visited upon Turtle Island, and created as a tribute to Archie Shepp, whose classic signature work of the Black Arts Movement, *Blasé*, had a profound impact upon the old Fred Ho. This recording is dedicated to Mr. Shepp.

This special edition release features the entirety of both texts, **SHE-WOLF** written by the late Ho and Ruth Margraff, and Stark's dark-as-night **MOMMA'S SONG**, as well as illustrations by Mac McGill to convey Fred Ho's musical manga imagination.

1

MOMMA'S SONG

Music and Concept by **Fred Ho**
Written by **Christine Stark**
Illustrations by **Mac McGill**

Fred Ho (baritone sax), Masaru Koga
(alto sax), David Bindman (tenor sax), Art Hirahara
(piano), Wesley Brown (bass), Royal Hartigan (drums),
featuring Jennifer Kidwell (vocals).

Recorded June 26, 2006 at Studio Masuo, NYC.
Mixed, Edited and Mastered July 2 and 28, 2006.
Engineer: Jon Rosenberg.

Published by Transformation Art Publisher (ASCAP), 2006.
Original music for Blasé by Dawn of Freedom Publishing (BMI), 1969.
www.spectrummusic.net / www.bigredmediainc.com

Supported in part by a grant from
the Aaron Copland Fund for Music Recording Program